Oxford University Press, Walton Street, Oxford OX2 6DP

Oxford New York Toronto
Delhi Bombay Calcutta Madras Karachi
Kuala Lumpur Singapore Hong Kong Tokyo
Nairobi Dar es Salaam Cape Town
Melbourne Auckland Madrid

and associated companies in
Berlin Ibadan

Oxford is a trade mark of Oxford University Press

First published 1990
Reprinted 1991, 1993

First published in paperback 1993

For Carolyn Haywood

Hardback ISBN 0 19 279878 2
Paperback ISBN 0 19 272267 0

A CIP catalogue record for this book is available
from the British Library

Typeset by Pentacor PLC, High Wycombe, Bucks.
Printed in Hong Kong

# Santa Claus
# takes off!

**Victor and
Glenys Ambrus**

Oxford University Press

OXFORD  TORONTO  MELBOURNE

A few weeks before Christmas, Santa Claus decided to make an early start from the North Pole. He was going to stay with his Auntie Flo, near the big city, so that he'd be ready to deliver all the presents on Christmas Eve.

The reindeer started to groan. They all complained they'd got headaches, stomach-aches, and back-aches. They didn't want to go on a long journey – they'd sooner stay at home. Santa took no notice and set off.

Auntie Flo was very pleased to see him. He parked his sleigh ready to be loaded with presents, and tucked up the reindeer in the garden shed to recover from the journey.

'Reindeer food is more expensive this year,' Santa told Auntie Flo. 'I just don't know how I'm going to pay for it all.'

'Why don't you get a job in Santa's Grotto in the big store,' suggested Auntie Flo. 'If they employ fake Santas, surely they'll give *you* a job.'

Some naughty children didn't believe he was real. They tugged at his beard to see if it would come off, until his chin felt quite sore. But there were plenty of nice children too, and Santa spent a long time talking to them. He sat them on his lap, gave them presents, and sent them away happy.

The queue outside Santa's Grotto grew and grew. Angry mothers complained, children squabbled, and babies cried.

TO SANTA

The manager gave him the sack. He wanted somebody younger, faster, and more efficient to get the children through the Grotto more quickly.

The Rent-a-Santa Agency sent a new fake Santa to deal with the queues. He got rid of the children in no time at all.

Santa was getting short of reindeer food. 'I'll have to cut down the rations,' he sighed.

But the presents came piling in. Instead of train-sets and dolls, it was skateboards, mountain-bikes, and computers. Santa hardly knew where to put them all.

He kept loading his sleigh for days and days. It got heavier and heavier, and the reindeer all complained again. But at last the Big Night arrived.

Santa cheered himself up with a cup of extra sweet tea, gave the reindeer a double ration of oats, and set out on his deliveries.

He had hardly got into the High Street when the reindeer all got back-ache and refused to move. Santa gave a push, then he gave a pull, but the sleigh wouldn't budge.

'I'll have to ring the Breakdown Service,' he said. 'It's a good job I've got a "Get You Home" insurance policy.'

Just then who should come round the corner but Police Officer Bertha. 'You are causing an obstruction,' she said, getting out her notebook.

'Bit of a problem, I'm afraid, Miss. Would you be kind enough to keep an eye on the reindeer for me while I phone for help?'

Bertha glared after him as he ran to the nearest telephone box.

'Sleigh broken down on the corner of High Street and Jubilee Gardens,' he gasped. 'Come quickly, please!'

He raced back and was just in time to see Police Officer Bertha slap a penalty ticket on Rudolf's back.

'Gotcha!' she snapped.

'But I'm Santa Claus! The one and only Father Christmas!' he pleaded.

'They all say that!' said Big Bertha with a laugh. 'I booked five of them outside the big store. Happy Christmas!' With that she strolled away and gave a ticket to a fire-engine.

Santa became a little less Santa for a while. He became just a very angry Claus. 'All those children with no presents!' he shouted.

Luckily the Breakdown Man arrived to tow him away. He even found space for the reindeer with bad backs.

When he got home, Santa looked around for other transport. He had a mountain-bike to deliver.

'Hooray!' he shouted. 'I haven't been on a bike for ages.' He did a few wheelies for practice and then set out in great style, with his sack full of presents.

After delivering the mountain-bike and the rest of the presents, Santa decided to travel back on a spare skate-board to refill his sack.

He jumped on it, shot off into the night, and did a few 'ollies' around Police Officer Bertha, who was out looking for burglars.

Then he delivered more presents on a pair of skis. 'Let's see if I can still do parallel turns!' he chuckled as he whizzed down the High Street, narrowly missing Bertha as she tried to book him for dangerous driving.

But when he got back home again, he felt exhausted. 'I'm not as young as I used to be,' he sighed.

Auntie Flo had gone to bed hours ago, so he made himself another cup of tea. He looked at the huge mountain of presents still waiting to be delivered. There was a very big one with his own name on it. It was from Auntie Flo.

'I'll open it now,' said Santa. 'It will cheer me up.'

Under the paper wrapping he found a large laundry basket with a very pretty coloured bedspread in it.

'This will come in handy,' he said, and began unfolding his present.

But he discovered the 'bedspread' was an enormous bag with lots of strings attached to it, and also in the basket there was a burner to produce hot air.

He had a hot air balloon! It was made of beautiful patches of material, lovingly collected by his Auntie over the years.

His yells of delight woke up Auntie Flo and together they wasted no time blowing it up. Soon a magnificently coloured huge balloon rose above the snow-covered roof-tops into the moonlit sky, with Santa and sacks of presents safely in the basket.

Auntie Flo waved her bed-cap until the balloon disappeared from view and then went back to bed.

As Santa drifted over the town, he spotted Police Officer Bertha on her way home. He zoomed down to wish her a Happy Christmas but landed on double yellow lines by mistake.

'Oops!' he said, and took off again, with Officer Bertha leaping up and down, trying to stick on yet another parking ticket.

As the balloon shot away she went with it, clinging on to the side of the basket.

'He-e-elp!' she squealed. 'Let me down at once!'

'Not until you help me to deliver these presents to all the children!'

'Anything, anything!' she screeched.

So Santa hauled Bertha into the basket. She had to blow up lots of little balloons - she had plenty of hot air - and tie presents to the strings. They floated along the roof-tops, and gently let the balloons drift down the chimneys, popping the bigger presents through the open windows.

When she had got over her fright, Bertha gradually began to enjoy the trip, and began to sing in a squeaky high-pitched voice, 'I'm flying through the aaaaiir-!'

At last, all the presents were delivered, and they made their way back to Auntie Flo's courtyard where the reindeer lay recovering from their back-aches.

Santa held a sprig of mistletoe over Bertha and shouted 'Merry Christmas, Bertha! Give us a kiss!'

'You go and run!' said Bertha but she wasn't really angry.

'Oh, well, you can't win them all,' laughed Santa, and they all had a nice cup of tea instead.